Snip, Snip!

Written by Adam and Charlotte Guillain

It was the end of the summer holidays. Everyone who lived on Comet Street was having a barbecue.

While the adults cooked the food, the children played tennis on the lawn.

"I only missed the ball because I couldn't see properly!" Tess complained. "My fringe is in the way!"

"Mine too!" Finn laughed.

"And mine," said Rav. "Maybe we need to borrow some of my sister's hair clips!"

Asha's dad laughed. "You all need haircuts!" he said, as the children sat down to eat.

"The mobile hairdresser is coming tomorrow," said Mrs Joshi. "I'll see if she can fit you all in."

The next day, Tess and Finn's parents took them to Rav's flat.

"I don't need a haircut!" protested Tess, as she tripped into the room.

"You can't even see where you're going," Asha giggled.

Tess threw herself down on to the sofa and picked up a comic. But her fringe was so long she couldn't read the words.

When the hairdresser had finished with Alpa,
she asked who was next.

"Might as well get it over with," Rav said with a sigh.
Soon he was looking very smart.

Next, Asha sat down with a smile and chatted to the hairdresser.

"I love having my hair cut," she said, as she admired her hair in the mirror.

"You go next," Tess told Finn, looking at the clock.

Finn glanced at Rav. "Please can you cut my hair like his?" he asked.

When Finn was finished, the hairdresser glanced at her watch. "I'm afraid I've got to go in five minutes," she said.

"Just enough time for Dylan's hair," Tess told her mum. "I can wait until next time!"

As the hairdresser packed up her things, Tess's mum looked at Tess and sighed.

"You'll be all hot and bothered when you go back to school tomorrow," Mrs Harrison said.

The next morning, Tess scooted along the pavement with her fringe in her eyes.

The class had a new teacher called Mrs Knight. But when she wrote on the whiteboard, Tess struggled to see.

"Do you want to borrow a hair clip?" whispered Asha.

"No thanks, I'm fine," said Tess.

After lunch, Mrs Knight got some clay out.

"Pottery!" said Asha. "Brilliant!"

But Tess kept getting clay in her hair.

"My pot's rubbish," moaned Tess.

After school, Finn went to his swimming lesson.

"You look fed up," Tess's mum said to her. "Do you want to come to the wildlife park? Some new animals have just arrived!"

Tess agreed, but she felt tired and hot when they got to the wildlife park. She followed her mum over to the new animal enclosure.

Tess stared at the alpacas' hairy faces.

"Their fringes are longer than mine!" she giggled. "They need a haircut."

"That's just what they're about to get!" Mrs Harrison said with a smile.

Another keeper came into the enclosure and he held one of the alpacas still.

Tess gasped as he switched on the electric shears. "Will it hurt?" she asked.

"It doesn't hurt a bit!" called the keeper, shearing the alpaca.

When he had finished, he trimmed the hair out of the alpaca's eyes. *SNIP, SNIP!*

"She's much happier now!" said Mrs Harrison.

Tess patted the trimmed alpaca while the others were sheared.

"There," she whispered. "That wasn't so bad, was it?"

The alpaca nuzzled Tess's face and pushed her hair out of her eyes.

On the way home, they stopped at the supermarket. As they carried their shopping bags to the car, Tess blew her hair out of her eyes to look up at a sign.

"Can we just pop in here, Mum?" said Tess.

"What a good idea," said Mrs Harrison with a grin.

Tess had forgotten what it was like to see properly!
That evening, she didn't miss the tennis ball once.

"Can I play too?" asked her dad.

Tess took one look at his hair.

"You'll need a haircut first," she said. "Snip, snip!"

Talk about the story

Answer the questions:

1 What game were the children playing at the beginning of the story?

2 What does the word 'mobile', on page 4, mean?

3 What did Tess keep getting in her hair at school?

4 What were the new animals at the wildlife park?

5 Why did the alpacas need a haircut?

6 Why did Tess ask her mum if they could pop into the shop at the end of the story?

7 Why do you think Tess changed her mind in the end about getting her hair cut?

8 Have you ever avoided doing something like Tess did in the story? What was it?

Can you retell the story in your own words?